MAKE YOUR OWN ADVENTURE

The Hunt for SNUFFLEGRUNT'S TREASURE

Illustrations by Colin Petty
Written by Stewart Cowley

HAMLYN

Published 1985 by
Hamlyn Publishing,
A division of
The Hamlyn Publishing Group Ltd.,
Bridge House, London Road,
Twickenham, Middlesex, England.

Produced for Hamlyn Publishing by
Victoria House Publishing Ltd.,
4/5 Lower Borough Walls,
Bath BA1 1QR, England.

Printed in Belgium.

ISBN 0 600 31052 3

THE ADVENTURE

The Valley Folk need your help. Someone has stolen their treasure! To find it, they must go on a long journey, but they are not sure of the way — there are so many choices. You must make up their minds for them.

As you read the story, you will discover that there are decisions to be made — look for the signposts on the pages. Often there will be two choices, and a different page number beside each one. When you have decided what the Valley Folk should do, turn to the page number shown, and discover where you have led them!

Have a good adventure, and remember, the choice is yours!

One afternoon, the Valley Folk gathered outside Muchgrin's house. They were all sad, because they had each lost one of their favourite things. Muchgrin couldn't find his happy hat. Primrose had lost her best bracelet. And the Mayor's gold chain had vanished. Someone had visited the village in the night — and left behind a trail of giant footprints.

6

THE TRAP 8

THE FOOTPRINTS 12

"Only Snufflegrunt has such big feet," said Muchgrin. "He must be the thief."

"Oh dear," shivered Bluehat. "He's very fierce, isn't he? What shall we do?"

Should the Valley Folk set a trap? Or should they follow the footprints?

"I know," said the Mayor. "If we put all our best things in the Village Meeting House, Snufflegrunt will have to go there to get them. Then we can catch him!"

So they piled all their favourite things into the Meeting House, and climbed into the roof. There they waited, holding a big net.

Soon they heard a strange, sniffling noise. "Here he comes," whispered Muchgrin. "Get ready."

But when they saw who it was, it wasn't Snufflegrunt at all.

"Oh no!" cried the Mayor. "It's Little Wiffle, Snufflegrunt's little brother."

"Drop the net!" shouted Muchgrin.

"Wait!" said the Mayor. "Let him go. We could follow his trail to our lost treasure!"

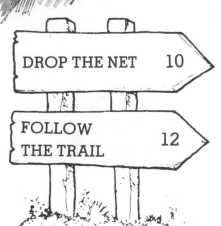

DROP THE NET 10

FOLLOW THE TRAIL 12

9

But Little Wiffle was only a baby, and when the net fell on him he jumped with fright. "Help!" he called, and became so upset he started to puff little sparks everywhere!

Then in came Snufflegrunt. The Valley Folk took one look — and fled. He was enormous!

"I wonder why they have all run away?" said Snufflegrunt, surprised. "Oh, what a mess you are in," he said to Little Wiffle,

helping him out of the net.

Outside the Meeting House, the Valley Folk were discussing what to do.

"Wait until they go," said the Mayor. "Then we can follow them to their hideout in the morning."

"Pick up your sticks and charge!" shouted Muchgrin bravely.

FOLLOW THEM 12

CHARGE! 14

11

"Look, the footprints lead into the hills!" cried Muchgrin. It was early morning, and the Valley Folk were ready for their adventure. It was a long, hot climb up the slopes above the village! Giant birds circled in the sky above them.

"Phew!" gasped Bluehat. "I'm so tired. And thirsty!"

"I can hear a stream," said Muchgrin, setting off towards the edge of a forest. "Come on, let's get a drink and have a rest."

But before they could find the stream, they heard loud squawking noises above them. Looking up, they saw the giant birds diving towards them!

"Quick, everyone, hide in the forest," shouted Bluehat.

"But the birds may be friendly," declared Muchgrin. "Perhaps they can help us."

HIDE IN THE FOREST   22

WAIT FOR THE BIRDS   16

13

Shouting and waving their sticks, the brave Valley Folk charged into the Meeting House. What a noise they made! Snufflegrunt and Little Wiffle were so shocked they both breathed out bigger sparks than they had ever made before. Wisps of smoke curled up from the wooden floor.

"Look!" shouted Muchgrin. "They've set fire to the Meeting House. Get some water!" The Valley Folk sprang into action. Soon the flames were out. But where were Snufflegrunt and Little Wiffle?

"I think they went into the forest," said Bluehat.

"Oh no," said the Mayor. "I'm sure they headed for the hills."

"Let's toss a coin," said Muchgrin. "Heads we go to the hills, tails we go to the forest."

Which way up will it land?

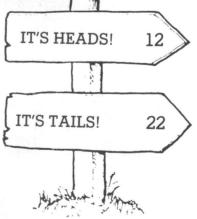

IT'S HEADS!   12

IT'S TAILS!   22

15

Muchgrin was right. The birds were friendly. They carried the Valley Folk high into the air so they could see for miles — except for Bluehat, who kept his eyes tightly shut! There was no sign of Snufflegrunt or Little Wiffle.

Soon the birds set them down. Sadly, the Valley Folk waved their new found friends goodbye.

"What a strange place," said Bluehat, looking around him. They were high up on the side of the mountain. There was no path, or any

THE RED DOOR
24

THE GREEN DOOR
18

sign of where they were. But in front of them stood two old doors, one painted red and the other painted green.

"Well, which is it to be?" asked the Mayor.

"Green's my favourite colour," said Primrose, going towards the green door.

"Come on, this way," called Bluehat, pushing open the red door.

17

The door led into a cave. It was dark and full of cobwebs. "No-one's been here for ages," thought Primrose.

"I'm tired," said Bluehat, following Primrose inside. "I wish . . ." But before he could finish, the cave began to glow. It was a magic cave and Bluehat had said the magic words. Strange writing appeared on the walls.

To go up, sing ra-ta-la-tiddle-um
To go down, sing dum-dum-da-di-dum

"Magic spells," gasped Muchgrin. "Well done, Bluehat. But which song shall we sing? Will we find Snufflegrunt up, at the top of the mountain — or down, deep inside?"

19

The Valley Folk found themselves whirled up, up and around, before they were set down in the prettiest garden they had ever seen, full of apple trees. It was in the middle of a great forest, which stretched as far as the eye could see.

"Listen," whispered Muchgrin. They could hear the sound of heavy footsteps. Then, from some apple trees nearby, they heard deep, loud voices.

"Giants," said Bluehat, unhappily. "This must be their garden."

"We must hide!" said Muchgrin. The little band tiptoed nervously

to the edge of the garden, where the forest began. There they found the entrance to a tunnel in the ground.

"It looks very deep and dark," said Bluehat, peering anxiously inside. Behind them the voices grew louder.

"Into the tunnel, quick!" cried Muchgrin.

"Let's hide in the forest!" said Primrose, who was just a little afraid of the dark.

THE TUNNEL 30

THE FOREST 22

It was cool and shady underneath the tall trees.

"Here's a path," said the Mayor. "Let's see where it goes." But the longer they walked, the taller and thicker the trees became.

The Mayor suddenly came to a halt, and all the others bumped into him. "Hey!" shouted Bluehat — but then he saw why the Mayor had stopped. A deep ravine lay in front of them, spanned by a rickety old bridge. Far below, a wide river flowed.

"That bridge doesn't look very safe," declared Bluehat.

"But we'll have to cross it," sighed Primrose. "There's no other way."

INTO THE RIVER 32

They stepped gingerly onto the bridge, which creaked and swayed alarmingly. Primrose held on tight to the Mayor's arm.

"Nearly there!" called Muchgrin. But just as he was about to reach the far side the bridge gave a loud groan, and collapsed beneath them.

"Help!" cried Primrose, clutching the Mayor even tighter.

Once through the door, the Valley Folk found themselves in the courtyard of an enormous castle. They crossed the courtyard and went inside.

"Oh! It's dusty and dark in here," said Primrose. There was a candle on the shelf beside the huge fireplace. Bluehat went to light it. But when he tried to lift it down there was a loud click, and a secret door slid open. Just then they heard slow, heavy footsteps in the distance.

"Those footsteps must belong to a giant," said Muchgrin. "Into the secret passage, quickly."

"No, wait," said Primrose. "He might know where Snufflegrunt lives!"

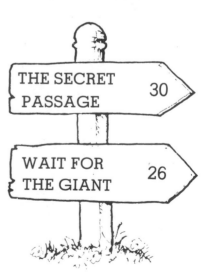

THE SECRET PASSAGE 30

WAIT FOR THE GIANT 26

The footsteps got louder and louder. A huge giant burst into the room. It was old Grumblefoot, and he was *very* cross.

"Aha!" he rumbled. "You must be the thieves who stole all my favourite things. I've caught you!" Before Primrose could say it wasn't them, Grumblefoot stretched out a big hand and blocked the

26

entrance to the secret passage. They dashed outside to the castle walls. Grumblefoot thundered after them. Far below lay a moat.

"Jump into the moat," cried Muchgrin.

"Back into the castle," puffed the Mayor.

THE MOAT   32

THE CASTLE   28

Keeping as close together as they could, they ran straight between Grumblefoot's huge legs before he could bend down and grab them. Back inside the castle they dashed into the first room they came to and shut the door. It was the giant's larder.

"Mmm, I'm hungry," said Bluehat. "Look at this." On the lowest shelf stood two baskets. In one were mushrooms, in the other apples. The labels read: *To find more of me, eat me!*

28

To find more of me, EAT ME!

To find more of me, EAT ME!

Outside, they could hear Grumblefoot searching for them.

"I think these are magic mushrooms and apples," said Muchgrin. "Which do you think we should try?"

"I'd like an apple," said Primrose.

"Mushrooms for me," said the Mayor.

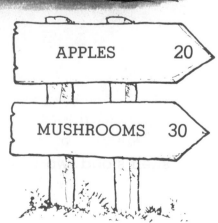

APPLES   20

MUSHROOMS   30

29

In the next instant they were in a dark tunnel. Everywhere clumps of mushrooms grew. "There's nobody here, but be careful, it's slippery," whispered Bluehat. They set off down the tunnel, but Primrose soon slipped up!

"Oh, oh, oh!" she squealed, knocking over Bluehat and the Mayor. They all fell over like skittles. The whole band slid helplessly downwards.

Down they tumbled, until they burst out of the tunnel onto a ledge. Below them lay a deep pool. Above, a hollow tree root hung down.

A rumbling noise grew in the tunnel behind them. Big mushrooms

came bouncing towards them. "It's an avalanche," shouted the Mayor above the din. "We must have started it when we fell!"

"Jump into the pool!" cried Bluehat.

"Climb up into the tree root, out of the way," shouted Muchgrin.

THE POOL 32

THE TREE ROOT 34

31

Muchgrin thought that they were going to fall for ever, but they soon hit the water with a mighty splash. "Is everybody here?" spluttered the Mayor as he paddled about.

"Yes," said Bluehat, "and I'm standing on something very strange!" The water swirled and everyone was lifted out of the water by a huge beast. It was Rumblebubble the Hippo!

"You seem to be in a spot of trouble," he burbled. Sitting down on his broad back Muchgrin told him why they were there. "You've got a long, hot journey ahead," said Rumblebubble. "You'd better

take this. It's a water flask that never empties." Then he carried them to the shore.

"Snufflegrunt's Treasure House is in the forest. Follow that path," he said, pointing to a gap in the trees. Thanking the gentle hippo, they set off once more.

THE TREASURE
HOUSE   38

Puffing and panting, the Valley Folk clambered slowly up the inside of the tree, finding cracks in the wood for their fingers and toes. It gradually grew lighter in the trunk, until at last Muchgrin could poke his head out of a large hole to see where they were. "We're outside again," he cried, and hopped through.

Everywhere they looked they saw lovely tree-houses.

"Er . . . hello," called Muchgrin, nervously.

THE TWIGGLY
KING 36 >

"Hello," answered a tall, green man. "Don't be frightened, we are the Twigglies and this is our village. I think you should come and meet our King. He likes visitors."

They followed the Twiggly until they reached the highest tree in the forest, where the Twiggly King lived.

"What have we got here?" beamed the Twiggly King from his leafy throne. Muchgrin explained who they were and how Snufflegrunt kept stealing all their favourite things.

"He's a terrible thief all right," agreed the King. "He even steals our favourite things sometimes! Have a rest for a while, then we'll show you the way to go."

The Valley Folk were tired and soon fell asleep. When they awoke,

the Twiggly King gave them a magic water flask that never ran dry, and took them to a broad path that led through the trees. "That's the way to Snufflegrunt's Treasure House," he said. "Good luck!"

Cheered by the kindness of the Twigglies, and feeling a lot braver, the Valley Folk set off along the path.

THE TREASURE HOUSE 38

The little band walked and walked. "We must be getting near," said Bluehat. "Look at all these things!" On the ground odd bits and pieces of treasure lay like litter. At last they came to a small clearing in the forest. There they found a bright blue door, painted with the words *Snufflegrunt's Treasure House*.

Muchgrin pushed open the door and went inside. The others followed, just a little bit scared. More treasure lay about the floor of Snufflegrunt's hallway. Bending down, Muchgrin picked up a shield of shiny gold. "This could be useful," he muttered to himself, and slung it over his shoulder.

Suddenly there was a loud, sniffling noise. The Valley Folk froze.

"I know what that is," said Muchgrin.

"It's Little Wiffle!" exclaimed the Mayor.

"Now what do we do?" squealed Primrose. The Mayor looked up and saw a narrow stairway.

"Climb up there," he cried.

"Charge him, come on everybody," shouted Muchgrin.

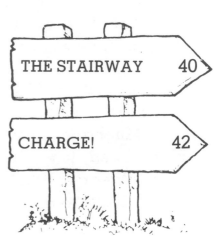

THE STAIRWAY 40

CHARGE! 42

As they climbed up the narrow stairs, they could hear Little Wiffle squeaking and sniffling unhappily at the bottom. Suddenly, Muchgrin stopped. "Don't push," he said. "We're on a very high ledge." They could see that they were in a huge cavern. Bluehat suddenly gave a startled cry.

"L-l-look! It's S-S-Snufflegrunt!"

There below them, the greedy dragon was rolling and wallowing in a huge pile of other people's favourite things. Then he looked up and

saw Muchgrin. He was so surprised that his mouth fell open. "Oooh!" he gasped, and out came a shower of hot sparks. The Valley Folk scrambled back down the stairway. In the rush, Muchgrin dropped his magic water flask into the cave.

Down it fell, turning over and over.

THE MAGIC FLASK
46

41

Shouting as hard as they could, the Valley Folk charged. Little Wiffle was jumping up and down, puffing out small clouds of hot smoke. The closer the Valley Folk got to him, the hotter they became.

"It's no good!" gasped Bluehat at last, skidding to a halt. "He's far too hot to get near!"

Little Wiffle, who wasn't really fierce at all, wanted to make friends. Shyly, he started walking towards the Valley Folk.

"What are we going to do?" cried Primrose. "I'm melting in this heat." The rest of the Valley Folk were beginning to feel faint too.

"I'll try to splash him with water from my magic flask. Dragons hate water!" cried Muchgrin.

Little Wiffle, who still didn't know what was wrong, was getting closer and closer . . .

CLOSER AND CLOSER 44

Muchgrin raised the magic flask and held out his golden shield against the heat. Little Wiffle gave a cry and ran. Poor Little Wiffle had seen his own reflection in the shield and frightened himself!

"Come on," shouted Muchgrin. "He's on the run." He dashed after Little Wiffle, with the Valley Folk close behind. They followed him onto a high ledge above a huge cavern. In the middle was Snufflegrunt, sitting on a mountain of other people's favourite things! But Little Wiffle couldn't stop. He ran straight off the ledge and landed right on top of Snufflegrunt! The two tumbled off the pile of treasure, steaming and puffing in surprise. The Valley Folk roared with laughter.

"You're so funny," giggled Primrose.

"Really?" answered Snufflegrunt. "Do you think so?"

"Yes," said Primrose. "And you're really quite nice." All of a sudden the dragons' fires went out! You see, dragons only huff and puff when they are frightened or nervous.

The Valley Folk went to help them up. "I didn't know I shouldn't take things," said Snufflegrunt. "I'd give them all back — but I do love them a lot!" He looked so sad that Muchgrin let him keep his happy hat, Primrose gave him her best bracelet, and the Mayor gave him his gold chain.

"Oh thank you!" said Snufflegrunt, beaming. "I promise I'll never ever take anything again!"

And he never did.

THE END

The magic flask fell right into Snufflegrunt's open mouth! He gulped. And he coughed. And then blew out a big cloud of steam. A happy smile spread across his face.

"His fire's gone out . . . his fire's gone out!" cried Muchgrin.

"Oh, thank you!" said Snufflegrunt. "I feel so much better. Here, you can have all these pretty things I've collected." Snufflegrunt just didn't know he wasn't supposed to take things!

The Valley Folk burst into laughter, and Little Wiffle was so pleased to find some friends, he agreed to go and get another magic flask to put *his* fire out. Well, would you like a fire in *your* tummy?

THE END

46